BASIC PNEUMATICS

PNEUMATIC SPEED CONTROL CIRCUITS

PNEUMATIC SPEED CONTROL CIRCUITS

INTRODUCTION

As previously described, pneumatic actuator speed is controlled by the air flow rate at the actuator. Flow rate can be changed either by changing the regulated supply pressure or by restricting flow with a needle valve.

This LAP will discuss the check valve and how it is combined with the needle valve to form the flow control valve, the valve most commonly used to control actuator speed. Then it will explain how to connect the flow control valve into different types of applications. These methods are called flow control or speed control circuits.

Selecting the correct speed control circuit for each application is a common design task for an engineer or designer. For the technician, this is also important because it helps to understand how to adjust these systems.

ITEMS NEEDED

Amatrol Supplied
  1 85-BP Basic Pneumatics Learning System
  1 85-IP Intermediate Pneumatics Learning System (optional)

School Supplied
  1 Compressed Air Supply
  1 Stop Watch

SECOND EDITION, LAP 4, REV. B

Amatrol, AMNET, CIMSOFT, MCL, MINI-CIM, IST, ITC, VEST, and Technovate are trademarks or registered trademarks of Amatrol, Inc. All other brand and product names are trademarks or registered trademarks of their respective companies.

Amatrol,Inc., 2400 Centennial Blvd., Jeffersonville, IN 47130 USA, Ph 812-288-8285, FAX 812-283-1584 www.amatrol.com

TABLE OF CONTENTS

SEGMENT 1

AIR FLOW CONTROL AND MEASUREMENT

OBJECTIVE 1	DESCRIBE THE MAIN FUNCTION OF A PNEUMATIC NEEDLE VALVE AND GIVE AN APPLICATION

The speed of a pneumatic actuator will be very fast if the load is small and there is little frictional resistance in the components. This speed is often too fast for the application so the actuator speed must be lowered. To do this, a needle valve is often used.

The main function of a needle valve is to control air flow rate by providing a restriction that creates an additional frictional pressure drop. Using a needle valve in a pneumatic circuit provides a means of speed control because it lowers the pressure at the actuator. Some typical pneumatic needle valves are shown in figure 1.

Figure 1. Typical Pneumatic Needle Valves

Almost all pneumatic cylinder applications use needle valves to control speed. Examples include a pneumatic robot, conveyor sorter gates, and clamps.

The needle valve, shown in figure 2, consists of two major components: a body and an adjustment screw. The valve body has two ports drilled into it with a passage connecting them to provide a flow path for the air. The adjustment screw varies the passage opening in the body from closed to fully open. The adjustment screw has a tapered end for very fine control of the orifice opening.

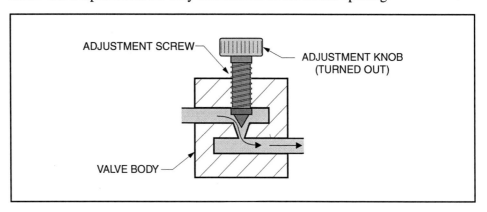

Figure 2.　Needle Valve

A needle valve controls the flow rate by causing a restriction of the flow. When the adjustment screw is turned all the way out, the passage is unblocked and has very little resistance to flow, as shown in figure 2. The further the adjustment screw is turned in (CW), the more the passage is restricted. This blockage causes more resistance to air flow, as shown in figure 3.

Air flow is restricted through this valve in the same way regardless of which direction the air flows through it.

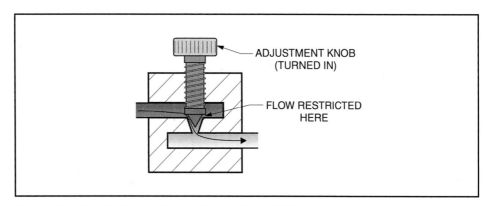

Figure 3.　Needle Valve Shown Controlling Air Flow by Restricting the Passage

The schematic symbol for a needle valve is shown in figure 4.

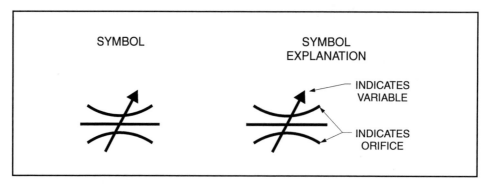

SYMBOL

SYMBOL
EXPLANATION

INDICATES
VARIABLE

INDICATES
ORIFICE

Figure 4.   Needle Valve Schematic Symbol

SKILL 1	CONNECT AND OPERATE A NEEDLE VALVE TO CONTROL ACTUATOR SPEED

Procedure Overview

In this procedure, you will set up a circuit to control the speed of the air motor. You will substitute a flow control valve for the needle valve. These two valves are the same except that the flow control valve has a component called a check valve in it. The check valve will have no effect in this circuit. You will learn more about flow control valves later.

❑ 1. Set up the circuit shown in figure 5.

Be sure to connect the flow control valve in the orientation shown in figure 5. The end of the valve which is not labeled with an "N" should connect to the supply line. If this were a true needle valve, the orientation of connections would not matter.

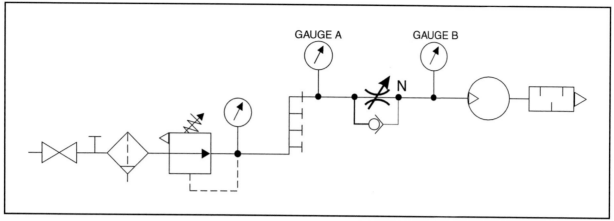

Figure 5.　Pneumatic Speed Control Circuit

□ 2. Turn the flow control valve's adjustment knob fully CW to close it.

□ 3. If not already connected, connect the compressed air supply source to the male quick-connect plug on the instrumentation module.

□ 4. Open the shutoff valve.

□ 5. Adjust the regulator pressure to 50 psi / 345 kPa.

□ 6. Turn the flow control valve's knob CCW 1 turn and observe the speed of the motor.

NOTE

Spin the shaft of the motor CCW by hand to see if it will turn on its own. If it does not, turn the flow control adjustment CCW slightly until the motor is able to sustain rotation. This should occur between 1 and 1-1/2 turns on most motors.

You should observe that it begins turning but at a slow speed.

❑ 7. Record the pressure readings at Gauges A and B in row 1 of the following chart. The difference in pressure is the pressure drop across the needle valve.

NEEDLE VALVE OPENING	PRESSURE (psi/kPa)		
	Gauge A	Gauge B	ΔP_{AB}
1 Turn	/	/	/
2 Turns	/	/	/
3 Turns	/	/	/
4 Turns	/	/	/
5 Turns	/	/	/

❑ 8. Calculate the ΔP for the 1 turn setting and record it in the chart above .

❑ 9. Repeat steps 4-6 for each of the other settings in the chart. As you do this, observe the speed of the motor.

You should observe that as the ΔP across the needle valve becomes lower, the motor speed becomes higher. This is because there is more DP being applied to the motor. The ΔP applied to the motor is the same as that shown by Gauge B because the pressure at the motor exhaust is near zero. Remember that the total ΔP available is 50 psi / 345 kPa. If more of it is used by frictional resistance, the motor will turn slower.

❑ 10. Experiment with your ability to change the motor speed by adjusting the setting of the needle valve.

❑ 11. Turn the regulator adjustment CCW fully to reduce the flow rate to zero.

❑ 12. Close the shutoff valve.

❑ 13. Remove the hoses and store them.

The flow rate of air is the amount of air that passes through a system or past a point in a certain amount of time, as shown in figure 6. This amount can be measured either as a weight or a volume. In pneumatics, air flow is most often measured by volume.

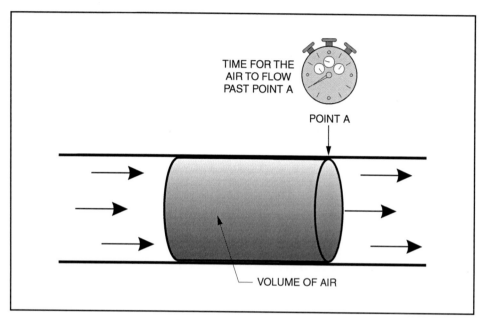

Figure 6. Volume of Air Flow in a Tube

For larger flows, the most common units of measure are cubic feet per minute (CFM) in the U.S. Customary system and cubic meters per minute (CMM) in the S.I. metric system. Smaller flow rates use an hour for the time instead of a minute. In this case, the units of measure would be cubic feet per hour (CFH) and cubic meters per hour (CMH).

Because air is compressible, the volume flow rate of air must be defined at a specific pressure. To properly size pneumatic components, it is important to understand exactly for which pressure the flow rate is defined. In pneumatics, three pressures are commonly used to describe air volumes:

- Volume at a given pressure
- Free air volume
- Standard Volume

It is not important which method is used; it is only important that the same method is used throughout all calculations.

Volume at a Given Pressure

This method defines the volume flow rate at the pressure that exists at the point of use. For example, the flow through the tube, shown in figure 7, is described as 3 CFM at 44.1 psi. This means that a volume of three cubic feet of air at a pressure of 44.1 psi passes by a certain point each minute.

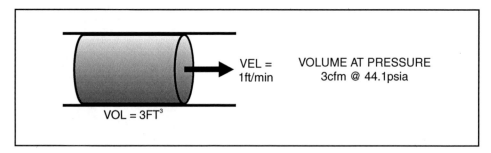

Figure 7.   Volume Flow Rate at a Given Point

Power output devices, such as pneumatic tools, commonly specify flow rate requirements in this manner. In this case, the pressure specified is the pressure that would exist at the inlet to the tool.

Free Air volume

Free air volume describes the amount of volume the air flowing in the tube would occupy if it were allowed to expand to atmospheric conditions. For example, if we were to describe the air flow rate, shown in figure 7, in terms of free air, the volume flow rate would be much larger because the pressure of free air is lower. This is shown in figure 8.

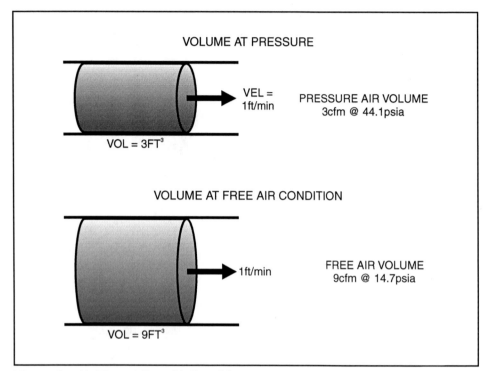

Figure 8.   Air Flow at Free Air Conditions

In many cases, the pressures in branch circuits of a pneumatic system are different, as shown in figure 9. For this reason, free air is often used to describe the air flow in these branch circuits even though the air flow in each branch is not at free air pressure. This allows designers to perform tasks such as calculating the total flow needed from the air compressor.

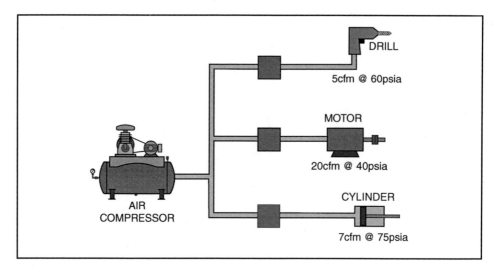

Figure 9.   Compressor Supplying Three Demands

Standard Volume

The third method of representing flow rate is the standard volume.

A standard cubic foot of air is defined as the existing number of molecules of air in a cubic foot of space at 68° fahrenheit and 36% relative humidity at sea level or 14.7 psia.

Because air conditions change from one location to another and from day to day, a standard reference is often used in order to compare the size of pneumatic components, especially air compressors.

To distinguish free air volumes from standard volumes, the word standard is used before the volume such as in "standard" cubic feet per minute or SCFM.

At sea level, free air and standard air are usually within 5% of each other. A later LAP will discuss more about standard air measurements.

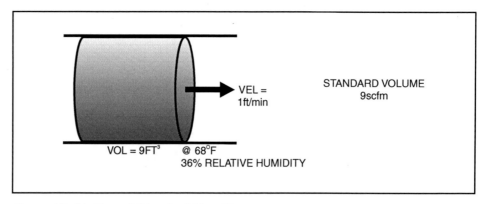

Figure 10. Air Flow at Standard Conditions

Procedure Overview

In this procedure, you will use Boyle's Law to convert volumes at pressures to the free air equivalent. In the first step, you will be given an example, then you will do it yourself. This is a common calculation used to determine the total air flow in a system when sizing piping, air compressors, and other components.

□ 1. Determine the free air volume equivalent of 65 CFM/1.85 CMM @ 80 psig/552 kPa.

VFA = _____(CFM/CMM)

The volume of air flow at a given pressure is easily converted to free air volume using Boyle's Law with 14.7 psia as the free air pressure, PFA, as follows:

FORMULA: FREE AIR VOLUME (V_{FA})

$$V_{FA} \times P_{FA} = P_1 \times V_1$$

U.S. Customary Units:

$$V_{FA} = \frac{P_1 \: x \: V_1}{14.7 \: psia}$$

S.I. Units:

$$V_{FA} = \frac{P_1 \: x \: V_1}{101 \: psia}$$

Where:

P_1 = *Pressure in tube (psia / kPa absolute)*
V_1 = *Actual flow rate of air in tube at pressure (CFM / CMM)*
V_{FA} = *Free air flow rate (CFM / CMM)*

This formula starts as Boyle's Law:

$$P_1 \times V_1 = P_2 \times V_2$$

If we use 14.7 psia for the final pressure, P_2, and V_2 as the free air volume, we get:

$$P_1 \times V_1 = 14.7 \: psia \times V_{FA} \: or \: 101 \: kPa \times V_{FA}$$

The formula is then rearranged to get:

$$V_{FA} = \frac{P_1 \: x \: V_1}{14.7 \: psia} \: \: or \: \: \frac{P_1 \: x \: V_1}{101 \: psia}$$

In this example, $P_1 = 80$ psig $+ 14.7 = 94.7$ psia and 552 kPa $+ 101$ kPa $= 653$ kPa. The final calculation is as follows:

U.S. Customary Units:

$$V_{FA} = \frac{P_1 \; x \; V_1}{14.7 \; psia}$$

$$= \frac{94.7 \; psia \; x \; 65 \; CFM}{14.7 \; psia}$$

$$= 418.74 \; CFM$$

S.I. Units:

$$V_{FA} = \frac{P_1 \; x \; V_1}{101 \; kPa}$$

$$= \frac{653 \; kPa \; x \; 1.85 \; CMM}{101 \; kPa}$$

$$= 11.96 \; CMM$$

❑ 2. An air drill has 5 CFM/0.14 CMM at 85 psig/587 kPa. Determine the air flow rate in units of CFM free air that must be supplied by the air compressor.

$V_{FA} =$ _____ (CFM/CMM)

The answer is $V_{FA} = 33.91$ CFM/0.095 CMM.

❑ 3. Three sizes of air jet weaving looms were purchased by a textile mill. Calculate the total flow rate the air compressor must supply in terms of free air to operate the three looms at the same time.

The air flow rate needed to operate each machine is as follows:

Airjet Loom A = 70 CFM/2 CMM @ 65 psig/448 kPa

Airjet Loom B = 110 CFM/3.1 CMM @ 50 psig/345 kPa

Airjet Loom C = 25 CFM/0.7 CMM @ 45 psig/310 kPa

To determine the demand, each volume at pressure would be converted to free air volume and added together as follows:

$$Vol_{Total \; FA} = V_{DrillFA} + V_{MotorFA} + V_{CylFA}$$

$V_{FATotal} =$ _____ (CFM/CMM)

The answer is V_{FA} Total = 965.2 CFM/27.4 CMM.

❑ 4. An air compressor available on a construction job site will supply a total of 150 CFM/4.26 CMM of free air. How many sandblasters can be used if they each require 10 CFM/0.3 CMM at 90 psig/621 kPa.

Number of sandblasters_____

The answer is 2 sandblasters.

Measurement of actual air flow rate is a task that must be performed in industry. It is used to verify the performance of both new and old components. Large air compressors, for example, often have a flow rate test performed when they are new to verify that the machine is working properly. Years later, this same test can be performed to troubleshoot the machine.

The best method for measuring air flow rate is to use a flowmeter. Several types of flowmeters are available. A common type is the rotameter, or variable orifice flowmeter. It is the type provided on the Amatrol trainer and is shown in figure 11.

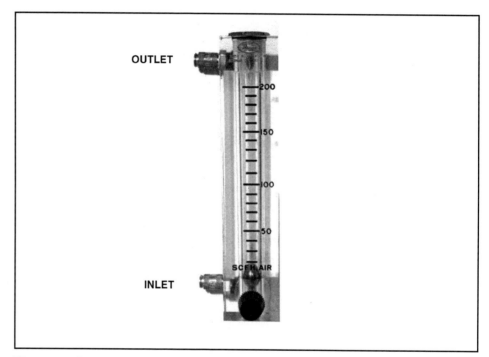

Figure 11. Rotameter Flowmeter on the Amatrol Trainer

The rotameter is a variable orifice flowmeter, consisting of a rectangular acrylic tube. The inside of the tube is tapered and round. Trapped inside is a metal ball of the required size and weight to match the calibration for standard flow. Inscribed on the outside is a scale, calibrated to show the flow rate when the ball center is aligned with the flow rate on the scale. The scale on the rotameter on the Amatrol trainer is calibrated in SCFH (standard cubic feet per hour) because you will be using low flow rates.

When flow enters the inlet (bottom), it passes around the metal ball at the small diameter of the tapered tube. The resistance to flow, between the tapered tube walls and the metal ball, builds up a pressure capable of raising the ball as flow increases. The ball floats upward until equilibrium takes place, as shown in figure 12. The pressure differential created balances the ball's weight. The name rotameter comes from the rotation of the ball due to air molecules colliding with slight surface irregularities invisible to the naked eye.

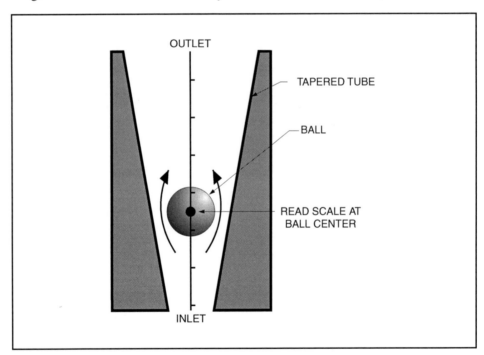

Figure 12. Diagram of Rotameter Flow Action

The schematic symbol for the flowmeter is shown in figure 13.

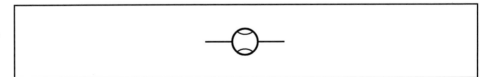

Figure 13. Schematic Symbol for a Flowmeter

Procedure Overview

In this procedure, you will connect the rotameter flowmeter to an air supply and measure the flow rate at different supply pressures.

☐ 1. Connect the rotameter as shown in figure 14.

Notice that this particular rotameter has a needle valve built into the inlet side of the flowmeter. The needle valve allows the user to open flow to the flowmeter slowly, preventing a sudden burst of air from shooting the ball to the top and causing possible damage.

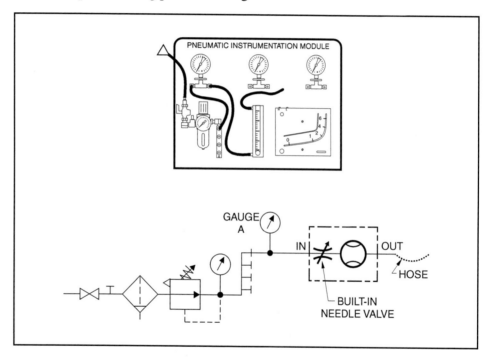

Figure 14. Schematic and Pictorial of the Rotameter Connected to Supply

CAUTION

To open the outlet of the rotameter, connect one end of a short hose to this port. When you perform this procedure, tie or hold down the loose end of this hose to avoid whipping and possible injury.

Normally, the rotameter does not have a fitting at the outlet and exhausts directly to atmosphere. However, in a later LAP, you will use the rotameter in a different application where you will need to connect to this port.

❑ 2. Perform the following substeps to adjust the needle valve on the rotameter.

    A. Close the valve completely by turning the black knob at the bottom of the flowmeter completely CW.

    B. Turn the knob six turns CCW to open the needle valve completely. This will remove most of the restriction of the needle valve from the circuit.

CAUTION

Do not exceed six needle turns or pressure may cause the needle valve adjuster to blow out.

❑ 3. If not already connected, connect the compressed air supply source to the male quick-connect plug on the instrumentation panel and open the shutoff valve.

❑ 4. Slowly turn the regulator adjustment CW until the pressure at Gauge A reads 10 psi / 69 kPa.

You should observe that the flowmeter ball rises and hear air exhausting from the flowmeter outlet.

❑ 5. Read the flowmeter by aligning the center of the ball with the scale and record the flow rate in the chart. You may observe a slight jiggle of the ball. Take the average value.

PRESSURE (psig/kPa)	FLOW RATE (SCFH)
10/69	
15/103.5	
20/138	
30/207	

❑ 6. Repeat steps 4 and 5 for the other pressures listed in the chart.

You should observe that an increase in pressure produces an increase in flow rate.

❑ 7. Turn the pressure regulator adjustment CCW fully to reduce the flow rate to zero.

❑ 8. Close the shutoff valve.

❑ 9. Remove the hoses and store them.

SELF REVIEW

1. To close a needle valve, turn the adjustment _____(CW/ CCW).

2. SCFH means _____.

3. The rotameter flowmeter is also called a(n) _____ flowmeter.

4. The needle valve controls the flow rate by providing a(n) _____.

5. The free air flow rate of 2 CFM at 58.8 psig is _____ CFM.

6. Larger air flow rates are usually specified as _____.

SEGMENT 2

FLOW CONTROL VALVES

OBJECTIVE 6	DESCRIBE THE FUNCTION OF A PNEUMATIC CHECK VALVE AND GIVE AN APPLICATION

The check valve allows air to flow in one direction but completely blocks air flow in the other direction. It is considered to be a one-way directional control valve. Figure 15 shows several pneumatic check valves.

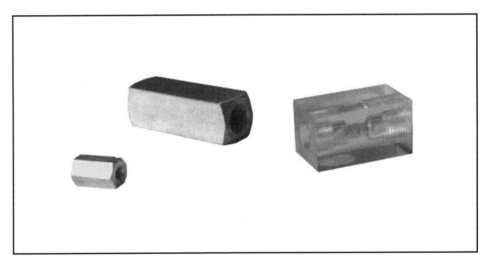

Figure 15. Pneumatic Check Valves

Pneumatic check valves have many applications. The circuit, shown in figure 16, shows four of the most common pneumatic applications of check valves. The explanation of each application is as follows:

- **Internal Compressor Valves** - Intake and discharge valves in piston air compressors are check valves. More will be discussed about them when air compressors are discussed in a later LAP.
- **Holds pressure in receiver** - Normally the compressor drive is shut down when the storage tank, or receiver, reaches the maximum desired pressure. A check valve located between the compressor and the receiver keeps the system from losing air pressure back through the compressor.
- **Quick-connect fittings** - Quick-connect fittings are used to rapidly connect and disconnect pneumatic components when flexible supply lines are used. The check valves are often built into these fittings so that air pressure in the supply line is not lost when it's disconnected.

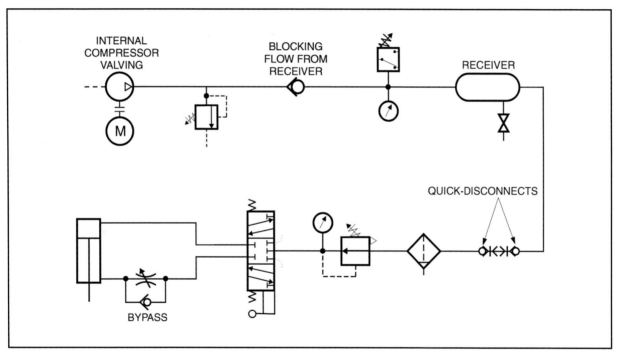

Figure 16. Four Common Pneumatic Check Valve Applications

- **Bypass -** Check valves are used in circuits to bypass the flow around certain components in one direction. This allows the component to control the circuit's operation in one direction and have no effect in the other direction.

  In the circuit of figure 16, the check valve is used to bypass the needle valve in one direction. This causes the needle valve to control the speed of the cylinder in one direction. In the other direction, the cylinder will move as fast as the pressure will allow.

  Specialized check valves are also used in the other applications. These applications include performing logic functions by selecting the higher pressure from two sources and blocking flow in event of line breakage to protect against hose whip. These valves and their applications will be explored in later LAPs.

There are two common types of check valves used in pneumatics:
- Ball
- Poppet

Cross-section sketches of each type along with the check valve symbol are shown in figure 17.

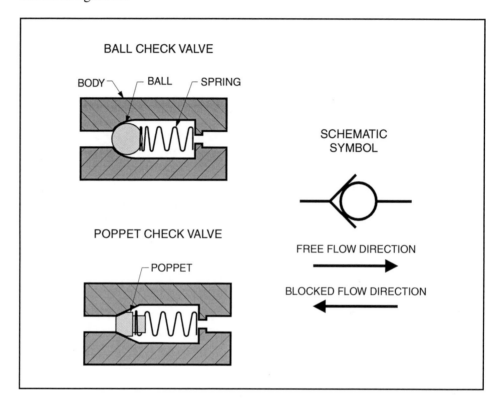

Figure 17. Common Types of Pneumatic Check Valves

Procedure Overview

In this procedure, you will demonstrate that a check valve placed in the cylinder line of a double-acting cylinder will allow the cylinder to move in one direction only.

❑ 1. Connect the circuit shown in figures 18 and 19.

NOTE

Just read this procedure if you do not have the Amatrol 85-IP Intermediate Pneumatic module. This skill uses the check valve that is supplied with the 85-IP module.

In this circuit, the cylinder and DCV are connected in a typical cylinder reciprocation circuit except that a check valve has been placed in one of the cylinder lines.

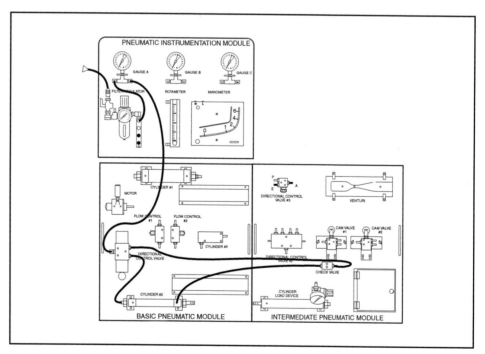

Figure 18. Pictorial of a Cylinder Reciprocation Circuit with Check Valve in a Cylinder Line

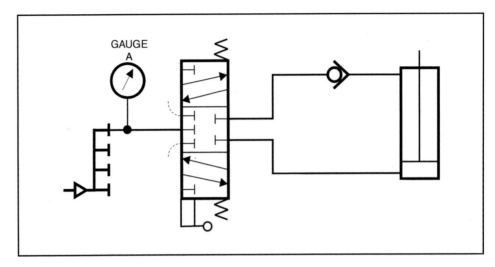

Figure 19. Schematic of a Cylinder Reciprocation Circuit with Check Valve in a Cylinder Line

❑ 2. If not already connected, connect the compressed air supply source to the male quick-connect plug on the instrumentation module and open the shut-off valve.

❑ 3. Turn the regulator adjustment knob CW until the pressure at Gauge A reads 10 psi / 69 kPa.

❑ 4. Push in on the lever of the DCV to extend the cylinder's rod. Continue holding the lever until the cylinder's rod is fully extended. Then release it.

You should observe that the cylinder extends with exhaust air flowing across the check valve in the free-flow direction.

This check valve uses a poppet and spring to control the flow of fluid through the valve. The spring is only strong enough to allow the poppet to block the passageway. A very low pressure, usually 0.5 to 3 psig (3.5 to 20.7 kPa), can push it open. The term "free flow" is used for fluid flowing in this direction (figure 20). The free flow direction of a check valve is often marked with an arrow on the check valve's body.

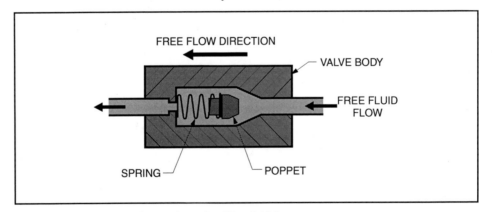

Figure 20. Free Flow Operation of a Check Valve

❑ 5. Now pull out on the lever of the DCV to retract the cylinder.

What happens? Does the cylinder rod retract or does it remain extended?

___

You should observe that the cylinder remains extended, because the check valve will not allow air to flow from the DCV to the rod end of the cylinder.

When the air tries to flow in the other direction, it pushes the poppet harder against the seat (figure 21). This completely blocks the flow of fluid through the check valve. This direction is called the checked, or blocked, direction. In the checked direction, these valves leak very little, if at all.

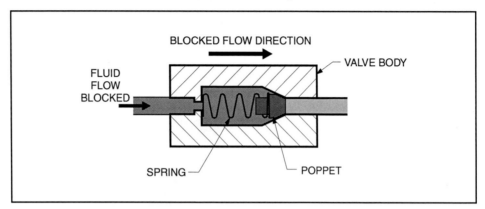

Figure 21. Blocked Flow Operation of a Check Valve

❑ 6. Release the DCV lever and switch the hoses at the check valve.

This will connect the check valve with the free-flow direction into the rod end.

❑ 7. Again pull out on the lever of the DCV to retract the cylinder. The cylinder should now retract.

❑ 8. Push in on the handle of the DCV to extend the cylinder.

You should observe that the cylinder now remains almost fully retracted because the check valve will not allow air to be exhausted from the rod end.

❑ 9. Release the DCV lever and close the shut-off valve.

❑10. Turn the regulator adjustment CCW fully to reduce the pressure to minimum.

❑11. Disconnect and store the hoses.

The flow control valve combines a needle valve and check valve together in one valve body to restrict flow in one direction and allow free flow in the other direction. Typical flow control valves are shown in figure 22. Notice that these look just like the needle valves of figure 1. It is usually difficult to tell them apart.

The flow control valve is a common method of controlling the speed of a bi-directional actuator in one direction only, because it reduces the plumbing required by not having to use a separate check valve.

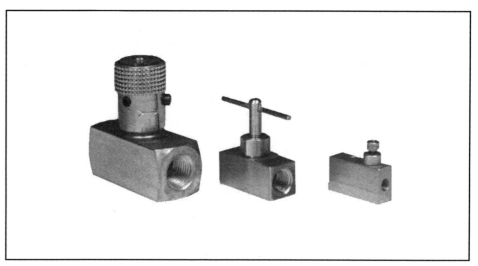

Figure 22. Pneumatic Flow Control Valves

The flow control valve consists of a body with two ports, a needle valve with an adjustment knob, and a check valve poppet, and a spring, as shown in figure 23.

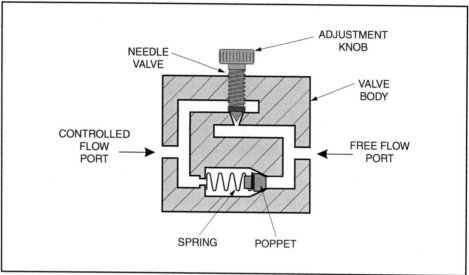

Figure 23. Construction of a Flow Control Valve

The two symbol techniques used for the flow control valve are shown in figure 24.

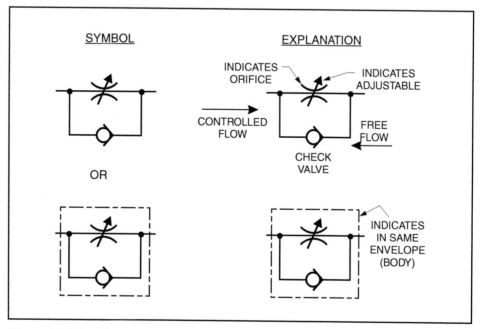

Figure 24. Flow Control Valve Symbol with Explanation

Procedure Overview

In this procedure, you will connect a flow control valve in a bi-directional actuator circuit to control speed in one direction only. You will see how a flow control valve connected in the circuit determines in which direction speed will be controlled.

❑ 1. Connect the circuit shown in figures 25 and 26.

In this circuit, the flow control valve will control the flow to a double-acting cylinder during extend. This will allow rod speed to be controlled during extend and run at full speed during retract.

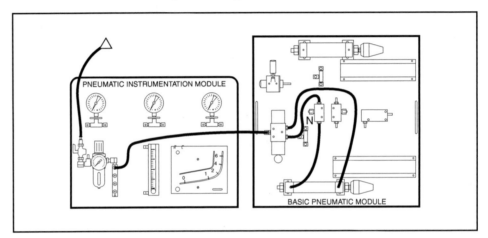

Figure 25. Pictorial of a Flow Control Valve in a Cylinder Circuit

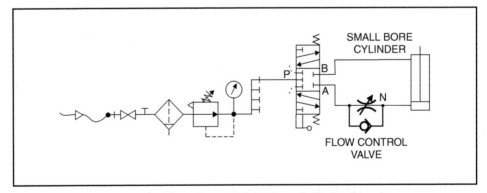

Figure 26. Schematic of a Flow Control Valve in a Cylinder Circuit

❏ 2. Perform the following substeps to connect the compressed air supply.

    A. If not already connected, connect the compressed air supply source to the male quick-connect plug on the instrumentation module.

    B. Open the shut-off valve.

❏ 3. Turn the regulator adjustment knob CW until the pressure at the regulator gauge reads 20 psi / 138 kPa.

❏ 4. Close the flow control valve completely by lifting and turning the black knob fully CW. Then open it 1 turn.

❏ 5. While watching the cylinder rod, push in on the lever of the DCV to extend the cylinder's rod. Continue holding the lever until the cylinder's rod is fully extended. Then release it.

You should observe that the rod moves slowly as it extends because the flow has been restricted by the flow control valve.

Air entering the flow control valve in the direction of controlled flow is forced to flow across the needle valve, as shown in figure 27. It cannot flow across the check valve, because the poppet blocks flow in that direction. The amount of flow, and therefore speed of the actuator, can then be controlled by adjusting the opening (restriction) with the adjustment screw.

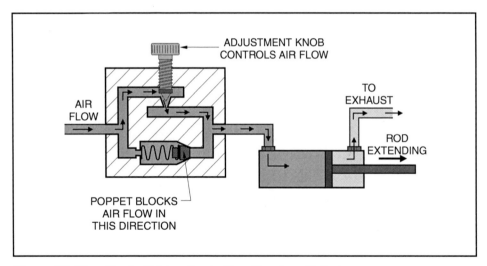

Figure 27. Flow Control Valve Controlling Flow to a Cylinder

☐ 6. Retract the cylinder by pulling out on the lever of the DCV. Continue holding until the cylinder's rod is fully retracted. Then release it.

You should observe rapid retract because flow through the flow control valve is in the free-flow direction.

Air entering the flow control valve in the direction of free flow can flow in two paths. It can flow across the opening of the adjustment screw and across the check valve poppet, as shown in figure 28. Because the poppet of the check valve opens fully to offer very little resistance, most of the air flow will take this path. The speed of the cylinder will then be at the maximum allowed by the flow of the system.

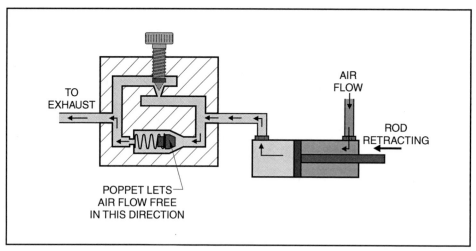

Figure 28. Free Flow Operation of a Flow Control Valve

☐ 7. Repeat steps 5 and 6 several times to cycle the cylinder. While cycling, turn the adjustment knob CCW one turn. Does the cylinder extend faster, slower, or stay the same? What about retract speed?

Extend Speed _____ (Faster/Slower/No Effect)

Retract Speed _____ (Faster/Slower/No Effect)

You should observe that the cylinder extends faster but the retract speed stays the same.

☐ 8. Now turn the adjustment knob 1/2 turn CW while cycling the cylinder. What happens now?

Extend Speed _____ (Faster/Slower/No Effect)

Retract Speed _____ (Faster/Slower/No Effect)

You should observe that the cylinder extend speed slows but little or no change occurs in the retract speed.

❑ 9. With the cylinder retracted, turn the regulator adjustment CCW fully to reduce the pressure to minimum.

❑ 10. Close the shut-off valve and move the handle of the DCV back and forth to remove all pressure from the circuit.

❑ 11. Now place the flow control valve in the other cylinder line, as shown in figure 29.

In this circuit, the flow control valve will control the retract speed of the cylinder.

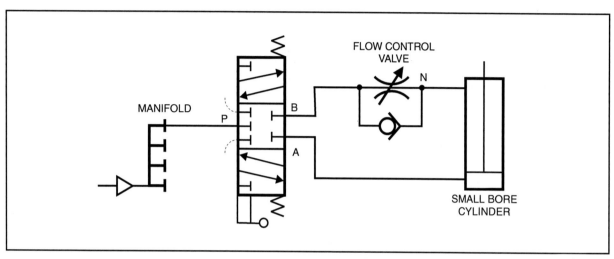

Figure 29.   Schematic of a Flow Control Valve Controlling Cylinder Retraction

❑ 12. Open the shut-off valve.

❑ 13. Turn the regulator adjustment knob CW until the pressure at the regulator gauge reads 20 psi / 138 kPa.

❑ 14. Close the flow control valve completely by lifting and turning the black knob fully CW. Then open it one turn.

❑ 15. While watching the cylinder rod, push in on the lever of the DCV to extend the cylinder's rod. Continue holding the lever until the cylinder's rod is fully extended. Then release it.

Now you should observe that the rod moves rapidly as it extends, because the air flow direction across the flow control valve is in the free-flow direction.

❑ 16. Retract the cylinder by pulling out on the lever of the DCV. Continue holding the lever until the cylinder's rod is fully retracted. Then release it.

You should observe that the rod moves slowly as it retracts, because the air flow is being restricted by the flow control valve.

❑17. Cycle the cylinder several times. While cycling, change the adjustment on the flow control valve and observe how cylinder speed is changed.

You should observe that only retract speed is changed with the flow control valve in this position.

❑18. With the cylinder retracted, turn the regulator adjustment CCW fully to reduce the pressure to minimum.

❑19. Close the shutoff valve and move the handle of the DCV back and forth to remove all pressure from the circuit.

❑20. Disconnect and store the hoses.

OBJECTIVE 10   DESCRIBE THE EFFECT OF ACTUATOR LOAD CHANGES ON FLOW CONTROL OPERATION

As you know, the air flow rate through either a flow control valve or a needle valve is determined by the restriction size and the pressure drop (DP) across the restriction. Once the flow setting is adjusted on either of these valves, the speed of the actuator is set. However, if the load at the actuator changes, speed will change.

This occurs because a change in load represents a change in the pressure requirement to move the load. This changes the DP across the flow control valve causing a change in the flow rate, thus a change in actuator speed. This means that flow control valves cannot maintain a constant actuator speed if load levels change.

Activity 1. Effect of Actuator Load Changes on Flow Control Valve Operation

Procedure Overview

In this activity, you will demonstrate that, while the valve is controlling flow, the flow rate through a flow control valve will change if the load at the actuator changes. Load changes will be simulated by changing the back pressure at the cylinder.

❑ 1. Connect the circuit shown in figure 30.

This circuit uses flow control A to control the extend speed of the cylinder and flow control B to apply back pressure (load) at the cylinder during extend. Gauge B will indicate the back pressure applied. Be sure to hook up the flow control valves exactly as shown.

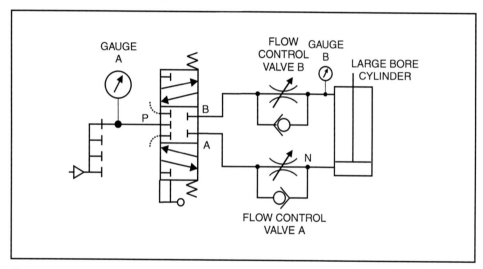

Figure 30. Schematic of a Cylinder Circuit to Apply Back Pressure During Extend

❑ 2. Perform the following substeps to connect the compressed air supply.

   A. If not already connected, connect the compressed air supply source to the male quick-connect plug on the instrumentation module.

   B. Open the shut-off valve.

❑ 3. Perform the following substeps to adjust the circuit for demonstration.

   A. Close flow control A by turning the adjustment fully CW. Then open it 2 turns.

   B. Open flow control B by turning the adjustment fully CCW. At this setting, the back pressure (load) during cylinder extend will be light.

   C. Turn the regulator adjustment knob CW until the pressure at Gauge A reads 40 psi / 276 kPa.

❑ 4. While cycling the cylinder by moving the DCV handle back and forth, measure and record in the chart the time to extend and the lowest pressure seen at Gauge B while extending. You should observe a fairly short time to extend and minimal back pressure at Gauge B. This would represent a light load during extension.

LOAD DURING EXTENSION	EXTENSION TIME (sec)	GAUGE B-BACK PRESSURE (psi/kPa)
Light		/
Heavy		/
Medium		/

❑ 5. Now put a heavy load at the cylinder by turning the adjustment on flow control B fully CW and then opening it 1/2 turn.

❑ 6. Repeat step 4.

   You should observe that the cylinder speed has slowed with an increase in load (Gauge B reading).

❑ 7. Decrease the load at the cylinder by turning the adjustment on flow control B another 1/2 turn CCW. This represents a medium load.

❑ 8. Repeat step 4.

   Comparing to the previous load, you should observe that the cylinder speed increases as the load (Gauge B reading) decreases.

❑ 9. With the cylinder retracted, turn the regulator adjustment CCW fully to reduce the pressure to minimum.

❑ 10. Close the shut-off valve.

❑ 11. Move the DCV handle back and forth to remove any pressure still in the circuit.

❑ 12. Disconnect and store the hoses.

1. The flow control valve consists of a(n) _____ valve and a(n) _____ valve in one envelope or body.

2. The two common types of check valves used in pneumatics are _____ and _____.

3. In a circuit where a flow control valve controls cylinder speed, a drop in the load will cause the cylinder to _____ speed.

4. Air entering the flow control valve in the _____ flow direction can flow two ways.

5. The check valve will allow flow in _____ direction(s).

OBJECTIVE 11	DESCRIBE THE OPERATION OF A METER-IN FLOW CONTROL CIRCUIT AND GIVE AN APPLICATION

Up to this point, this learning system has discussed the operation of the needle valve and the flow control valve without concern to the placement in the circuit. It has shown that these valves can be placed at either the inlet or the outlet of the actuator to control actuator speed. This placement, however, is important in some applications.

If the flow control valve is placed at the inlet to the actuator, it is called a meter-in flow control circuit, as shown in figure 31. In this example, the circuit affects the speed of the cylinder while it extends. Also, the fluid leaving the other end of the cylinder is allowed to leave unrestricted.

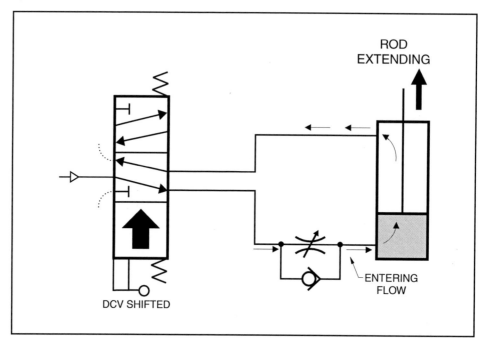

Figure 31. Metering-in to Control Cylinder Extend Speed

The meter-in flow control circuit can also be used to control the speed of the actuator during retraction if it is placed in the rod end line, as shown in figure 32.

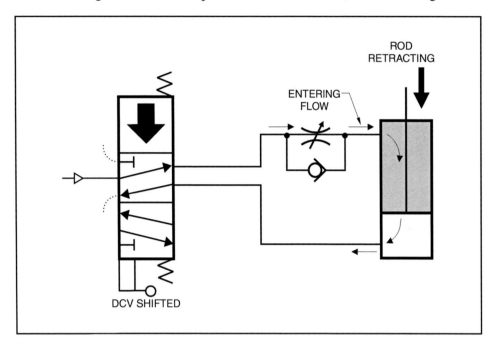

Figure 32. Metering-in to Control Cylinder Retract Speed

The meter-in circuit provides precise control and is a common method of controlling speed. However, it cannot be used in all applications. It can only be used to control speeds where the load opposes the rod movement. Extending the lift cylinder of a packaging machine is an example of an opposing load.

Procedure Overview

In this procedure, you will connect a flow control valve to meter in the flow and demonstrate the operation of this type of flow control circuit.

❑ 1. Connect the meter-in flow control circuit shown in figure 33. This circuit controls flow during extend only.

In this circuit, the flow control valve is positioned in the cylinder line that is connected to the cap (blind) end of the cylinder with its check valve blocking flow to the cylinder. Only flow through the adjustable restriction will determine cylinder speed during extension.

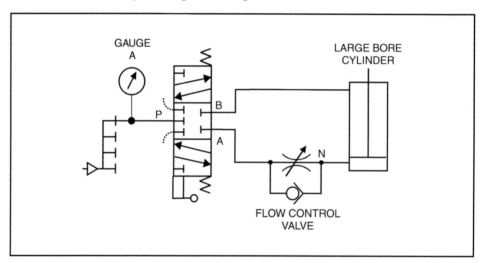

Figure 33. Schematic of a Meter-In Flow Control Circuit Controlling Cylinder Extension

❑ 2. If not already connected, connect the compressed air supply source to the male quick-connect plug on the instrumentation module and open the shut-off valve.

❑ 3. Turn the regulator adjustment knob CW until the pressure at Gauge A reads 30 psi / 207 kPa.

❑ 4. Close the flow control valve by turning the adjustment fully CW. Then open it 1/2 turn.

This setting will slow the speed of extension only.

❑ 5. Shift the DCV to extend the cylinder.

You should observe a slow extension, because air flow to the cylinder is being restricted by the variable orifice of the flow control valve.

❑ 6. Once the cylinder is fully extended, retract the cylinder and observe the speed of retraction.

You should observe a rapid retraction, because exhaust flow bypasses through the check valve minimizing the resistance to rod movement.

❑ 7. Cycle the cylinder several times to become more familiar with a meter-in flow control circuit.

❑ 8. Perform the following substeps to see how slowly you can get the cylinder to extend with meter-in.

A. While cycling the cylinder, close down the flow control valve to obtain the slowest, smoothest speed.

NOTE

You may have to extend and retract the cylinder several times to get the slowest setting.

You should observe that cylinder movement, while it extends, becomes "jerky," especially near the end of the stroke as the speed slows. This would not be the case if using hydraulics and is one of the disadvantages of pneumatic systems.

B. Record the slowest extend time obtained without jerky movement.

Time to extend _____(Seconds)

❑ 9. Turn the regulator adjustment CCW fully to reduce the pressure to minimum.

❑10. Close the shut-off valve.

❑11. Move the DCV handle back and forth to remove any pressure still in the circuit.

❑12. Disconnect and store the hoses.

Another method of controlling flow rate is a meter-out flow control circuit. This type, shown in figures 34 and 35, controls speed by restricting the flow of fluid leaving the actuator. The fluid entering the cylinder enters unrestricted.

Meter-out circuits control actuator speed well when the load is either aiding or opposing. This makes the meter-out circuit a more versatile method than the meter-in circuit.

The meter-out circuit is able to control speed when the load tends to run away (aiding loads) because it creates a back pressure on the piston. This back pressure is able to resist the force of the load. This back pressure also creates an opposing load at the cylinder to keep the cylinder in control with a solid cushion of fluid.

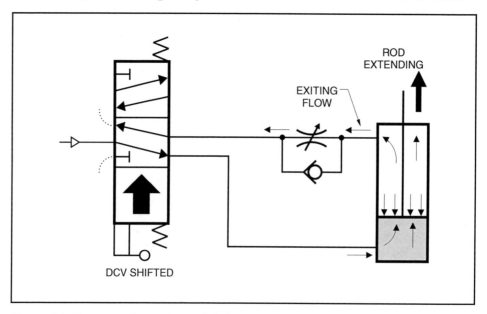

Figure 34. Metering-Out to Control Cylinder Extend Speed

The meter-out flow control circuit can also be used to control the speed of the actuator during retraction by placing it in the rod end line, as shown in figure 35.

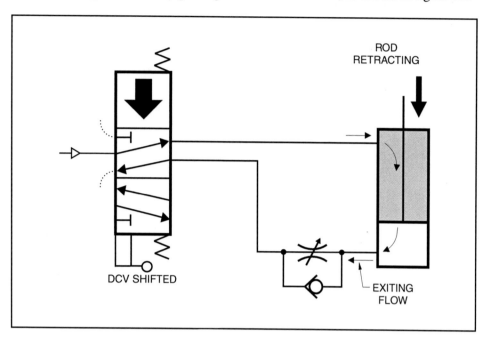

Figure 35. Metering-Out to Control Cylinder Retract Speed

In some applications, the load helps the rod movement in one direction. Retracting a packaging machine lift cylinder is an example where the load helps or aids the movement. The meter-in circuit will not work to control speed in these applications because the force of the load will tend to make the cylinder movement "run away."

Procedure Overview

In this procedure, you will connect a flow control valve in a meter-out flow control circuit and demonstrate the operation of this circuit.

□ 1. Connect the meter-out flow control circuit shown in figure 36.

In this circuit, the flow control valve will control the flow rate from the cylinder only when the cylinder extends. Gauge B will indicate the back pressure caused by the flow control valve.

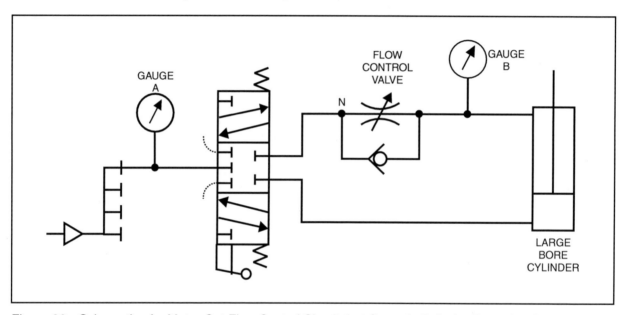

Figure 36.   Schematic of a Meter-Out Flow Control Circuit that Controls Cylinder Extension Speed

□ 2. Perform the following substeps to connect the compressed air supply.

A. If not already connected, connect the compressed air supply source to the male quick-connect plug on the instrumentation module.

B. Open the shut-off valve.

□ 3. Turn the regulator adjustment knob CW until the pressure at Gauge A reads 30 psi / 207 kPa.

□ 4. Close the flow control valve by turning the adjustment fully CW. Then open it 1/2 turn.

This setting will slow the speed of extension only.

❑ 5. Shift the DCV to extend the cylinder.

You may observe a jump in pressure on Gauge B as well as a jump in rod movement. This will be followed by a slow rod movement for the rest of the stroke with a constant back pressure on Gauge B. This initial jump is caused by the air being compressed between the cylinder and the flow control valve. This jump does not occur in hydraulics because the oil does not need to compress its volume as much to reach the pressure needed. For this reason, a hydraulic circuit will be much smoother.

❑ 6. Once the cylinder is fully extended, retract the cylinder and observe the speed of retraction.

You should observe a rapid retraction, because supply pressure bypasses through the check valve directly to the cylinder. Cylinder exhaust air flows unrestricted out the DCV exhaust.

❑ 7. Cycle the cylinder several times to become more familiar with the characteristics of a meter-out circuit.

❑ 8. Perform the following substeps to see how slowly you can get the cylinder to extend with meter-out.

A. Close down the flow control valve to get the slowest, smoothest extend speed. Smooth speed is determined when the needle of Gauge B does not wiggle and the rod does not jerk.

NOTE

You may have to extend and retract the cylinder several times to get the slowest setting.

B. Record the slowest time obtained without cylinder jerk other than the initial jump.

Time to extend _____(Seconds)

❑ 9. Compare this extend time to that obtained in Skill 2 for meter-in. Which time is longer?

You should have measured a longer time (slower extension) with the meter-out circuit. This shows that meter-out is a better method for slow speeds.

❑10. Turn the regulator adjustment CCW fully to reduce the pressure to minimum.

❑11. Close the shut-off valve.

❑12. Move the DCV handle back and forth to remove any pressure still in the circuit as indicated on Gauge B.

❑13. Disconnect and store the hoses.

Most pneumatic DCVs have exhaust ports that allow lines to be connected to these ports. This feature increases the number of circuits where the valve can be used. A common circuit is to connect a flow control or needle valve downstream of the exhaust of a 3/2 DCV to build back pressure and control the retract speed of a single-acting cylinder. This circuit is shown in figure 37. Notice that when the speed control valve is placed in the DCV exhaust line, the circuit is a meter-out circuit.

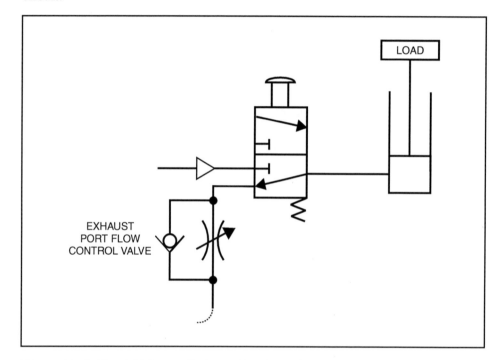

Figure 37. A Circuit Using an Exhaust Port Flow Control Valve

Applications for the exhaust port speed controls are with cylinders where loads can change periodically. One such application is with parts handling cylinders lowering parts from one level to another where the weight of the parts change from time to time.

Procedure Overview

In this procedure, you will connect a flow control valve in the exhaust of a 3/2 DCV to control the retract speed of a single-acting, spring return cylinder.

❑ 1. Connect the exhaust port speed control circuit shown in figure 38.

NOTE

Just read this procedure if you do not have the Amatrol 85-IP Intermediate Pneumatic Module. This skill uses the 3/2 DCV that is supplied with the 85-IP Module.

In this circuit the needle of the flow control valve will control the retract speed of the single-acting cylinder.

NOTE

You must connect a piece of hose to the N-port of the flow control valve to open the quick-connect.

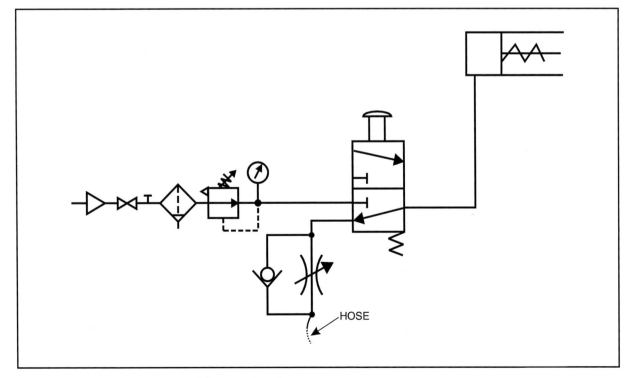

Figure 38. Exhaust Port Speed Control Circuit

❑ 2. Connect the compressed air supply to the instrumentation module and open the shutoff valve.

❑ 3. Turn the regulator adjustment knob CW until the pressure reads 30 psi/207 kPa.

❑ 4. Close the exhaust port flow control valve completely and then open it 1/2 turn.

This setting will slow the speed of retraction only.

❑ 5. Press the button of the DCV to shift the valve.

The cylinder should extend rapidly.

❑ 6. Now release the DCV button.

The cylinder should retract slowly.

❑ 7. While cycling the DCV, change the flow control setting and observe how the exhaust port speed control changes the speed of retract for this cylinder.

NOTE

The exhaust port speed control can also be used on 5-ported DCVs to control the speed of an actuator in either direction. With two exhaust port speed controls, a 5-ported DCV can control the speed of an actuator in both directions.

❑ 8. Turn the regulator adjustment CCW fully to reduce the pressure to minimum and close the shutoff valve.

❑ 9. Disconnect and store the hoses.

DESCRIBE THE OPERATION OF A PRESSURE PORT SPEED CONTROL AND GIVE AN APPLICATION

Another method of speed control is to place a needle valve or flow control valve in the pressure line of the DCV, as shown in figure 39. When this is done, it provides a meter-in circuit to the actuator. In bi-directional applications, the speed in both directions will be affected.

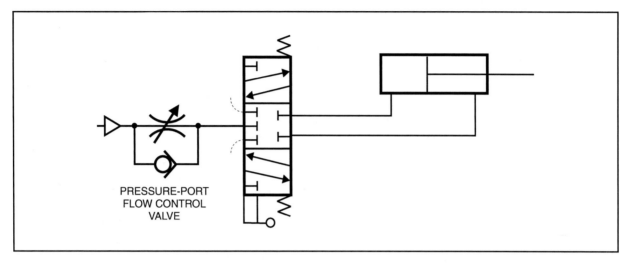

PRESSURE-PORT
FLOW CONTROL
VALVE

Figure 39.   A Circuit Using a Pressure Port Flow Control Valve

This method of speed control can only be used in applications where the load is opposing. One such application is to operate an agitator with a double-acting cylinder. The loads are always opposing and the speed in both directions will nearly be the same.

Procedure Overview

In this procedure, you will connect a flow control valve before the pressure port of a 5/3 DCV to control the extend and retract speeds of a double-acting cylinder.

❑ 1. Connect the pressure port speed control circuit shown in figure 40. In this circuit, the needle of the flow control valve will control the speed of a double-acting cylinder in both directions.

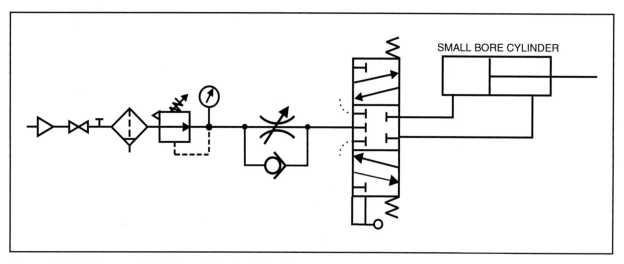

SMALL BORE CYLINDER

Figure 40. A Pressure Port Speed Control Circuit

❑ 2. Connect the compressed air supply to the instrumentation module and open the shutoff valve.

❑ 3. Turn the regulator adjustment knob CW until the pressure reads 30 psi/207 kPa.

❑ 4. Open the flow control valve fully (CCW).

❑ 5. Observe the speed of the cylinder as you shift the DCV back and forth.

The speed of the cylinder in both directions should be fast.

❑ 6. Now close the flow control valve and reopen it 1/2 turn.

❑ 7. Repeat step 5.

The speed of the cylinder in both directions should have slowed and be approximately the same.

❑ 8. While cycling the cylinder, change the flow control adjustment to several different settings to become more familiar with a pressure port speed control.

❑ 9. Turn the regulator adjustment CCW fully to reduce the pressure to minimum and close the shutoff valve.

❑ 10. Disconnect and store the hoses.

Procedure Overview

In this procedure, you will be given different speed control circuits to design and asked to draw their circuit schematics.

❑ 1. On a copy of figure 41, complete the drawing of a meter-out flow control circuit that controls the retract speed of a single-acting cylinder. The flow control valve is to be placed between the N.C. 3/2 lever-operated DCV and the cylinder. Start with the supply line shown and include a filter and regulator.

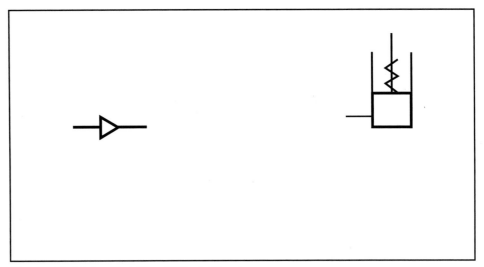

Figure 41. Meter-Out Circuit Work Sheet

❑ 2. On a copy of figure 41, complete the drawing of a pressure port speed control circuit. Start with the supply line shown and include a filter and regulator.

❑ 3. On a copy of figure 42, complete the drawing of a speed control circuit that provides meter-in speed control to a bi-directional motor in one direction only. A 5/3 lever operated DCV is to be used to change motor direction. Start with the supply line shown and include a filter and regulator.

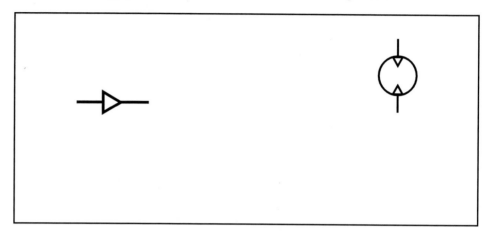

Figure 42. A Meter-In (One Direction), Bidirectional Motor Work Sheet

❑ 4. On a copy of figure 43, complete the drawing of a speed control circuit that provides exhaust port speed control during extend to a double-acting cylinder. A 5/3 DCV, lever-operated, is used to cycle the cylinder. Start with the supply line and include a filter and regulator.

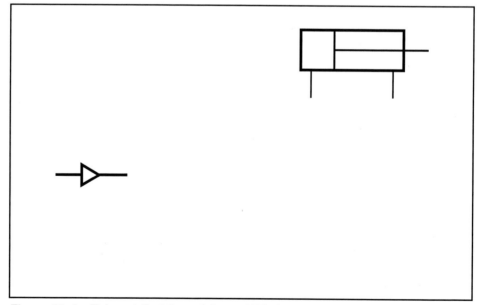

Figure 43. An Exhaust-Port Speed Control Work Sheet

❑ 5. Place a copy of your four designs in your portfolio. This is a part of your skills assessment.

In most cases, an industrial actuator's speed in each direction must be adjusted separately. This is called independent speed control. The reasons for this need include:

- **Slow Approach/Fast Reset** - Machines often require a cylinder to extend very slowly while it is performing an action. If the retract stroke is used only to reset the cylinder for the next cycle, it is desirable to retract at high speed to cut the cycle time. An example is the forming press shown in figure 44. This machine requires the cylinder to slowly extend while it is pressing the material. The cylinder can retract at high speed to reset for the next part.
- **Identical Speeds** - Because the rod and cap end areas of a cylinder are different, a cylinder will naturally extend and retract at different speeds. If the speed must be the same in both directions, the separate flow control valves must be used.

Figure 44. Forming Press with Slow Extend/Fast Retract

Procedure Overview

Independent speed control requires two flow control valves. One valve controls the speed in each direction. These valves can be connected to provide either meter-in or meter-out speed control.

In this procedure, you will design and connect circuits that will separately control the speed of an actuator in each direction.

□ 1. Complete the circuit shown in figure 45 so that you can control the speed of the double-acting cylinder in each direction using a separate flow control valve. Draw the two flow control valves so each valve provides meter-out flow control.

Label your flow control valves FC1 and FC2. FC1 should control the extend speed and FC2 should control the retract speed.

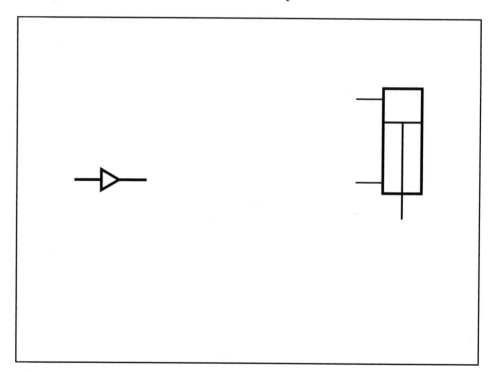

Figure 45. Partial Circuit to Control the Speed of a Double-Acting Cylinder

❑ 2. Connect your circuit design on the 850 Series trainer.

❑ 3. If not already connected, connect the compressed air supply source to the male quick-connect plug on the instrumentation module and open the shut-off valve.

❑ 4. Turn the regulator adjustment knob CW until the pressure at Gauge A reads 50 psi / 345 kPa.

❑ 5. Close both flow control valves fully and then open each one complete turn.

❑ 6. Now extend and then retract the cylinder. Notice whether the speed is controlled in both directions.

You should observe that the speed is controlled in both directions.

Confirm your design with the data sheet solution. This is a classic circuit design that designers often use in pneumatic circuits.

❑ 7. Adjust FC 1 to several different settings to test its effect on the circuit. Extend and retract the cylinder after each new adjustment and observe the cylinder's speed.

You should observe that the speed of the cylinder changes for only one direction of motion when FC 1 is readjusted. Record below which direction of motion changes.

FC 1 controls_____ (Retract/Extend)

You should observe that only the extend speed is affected.

❑ 8. Reset FC 1 to one turn open.

❑ 9. Now adjust FC 2 to several different settings to test its effect on the circuit. Extend and retract the cylinder after each new adjustment and observe the cylinder's speed.

You should observe that the speed of the cylinder changes for only one direction of motion when FC 2 is readjusted. This should be the direction opposite that of FC 1. Record below this direction.

FC 2 controls_____ (Retract/Extend)

❑ 10. Turn the regulator adjustment CCW fully to reduce the pressure to minimum.

❑ 11. Close the shut-off valve.

❑ 12. Move the DCV handle back and forth to remove any pressure still in the circuit.

❑13. Complete the circuit shown in figure 46 so that you can control the speed of a single-acting cylinder in each direction, using an exhaust port flow control valve to control retract speed. Use a 3/2 N.C. DCV to cycle the cylinder.

Label your flow control valves FC1 and FC2. FC1 should control the extend speed and FC2 should control the retract speed.

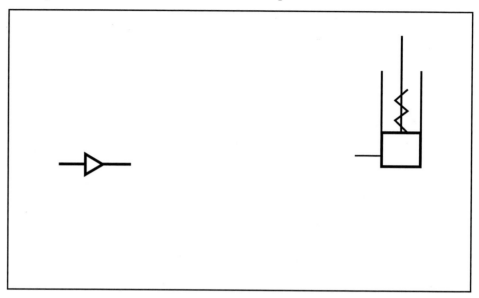

Figure 46. Partial Circuit to Control the Speed of a Single-Acting Cylinder in Both Directions

❑14. Now connect your circuit design on the 850 Series trainer. To open the exhaust side of the retract speed control, a hose must be connected to open the quick-connect. Tie or hold down the loose end of this hose when operating the circuit.

NOTE

Just read the rest of this procedure if you do not have the Amatrol 85-IP Intermediate Pneumatic Module. The 3/2 DCV is located on this module.

❑15. Open the shutoff valve.

❑16. Turn the regulator adjustment knob CW until the pressure at Gauge A reads 50 psi/345 kPa.

❑17. Close both flow control valves fully and then open each one complete turn.

❑18. Now extend and retract the cylinder. Notice whether the speed is controlled in both directions.

You should observe that the speed is controlled in both directions.

Confirm your design with the data sheet design. This is a classic circuit design that designers use to control the speed of single-acting cylinders.

19. Adjust FC1 to several different settings to test its effect on the circuit. Extend and retract the cylinder after each new adjustment and observe the cylinder's speed. You should observe that only the extend speed changes.

20. Reset FC1 to one turn open.

21. Now adjust FC2 to several different settings. Extend and retract the cylinder after each new adjustment and observe the cylinder's speed.

    You should observe that only the retract speed changes.

22. Turn the regulator adjustment CCW fully to reduce pressure to minimum.

23. Close the shutoff valve.

24. Disconnect and store the hoses.

1. Meter-_____ flow control circuits are used when the load is aiding or over-running.

2. A meter-out flow control circuit works well when the load is _____.

3. The two common circuit methods for controlling the speed of an actuator are called _____ and _____.

4. A meter-in flow control circuit controls speed by controlling the amount of air going _____ the actuator.

5. A meter-out circuit controls the speed of a cylinder by creating _____ on the piston.

6. The _____ speed control circuit uses separate flow control valves to control the speed of an actuator in both directions.

7. _____ port speed controls always provide a meter-in circuit.